Connected  Mathematics™

Assessment Resources

Grade 6

Prentice Hall

Glenview, Illinois
Needham, Massachusetts
Upper Saddle River, New Jersey

ISBN 0-13-053119-7

5 6 7 8 9 10   05 04

Assessment Resources

for
Grade 6

This book contains assessment resources for the following units:

Use the side tabs in this book to locate the desired unit. The page numbers listed match those of the pages in the back of the Teacher's Guide for that unit.

Assessment Resources

for
Prime Time

Check-Up 1

In 1 and 2, list all the factors of each number.

1. 35

2. 54

In 3 and 4, list all the proper factors of each number.

3. 42

4. 47

5. Which of the numbers in questions 1–4 are prime numbers?

6. Which of the numbers in questions 1–4 are composite numbers?

7. Which of the numbers in questions 1–4 are even numbers?

8. Is the sum of an odd number and an even number odd or even? Explain.

Quiz A

1. Suppose you are playing the Factor Game on the 30-board. Your opponent goes first and chooses 29, giving you only 1 point. It is now your turn to choose a number. Which number would be your best move? Why?

2. Suppose the person who sits next to you was absent the day you played the Factor Game. On the back of this paper, write a note to him or her explaining the strategies you have discovered for winning the Factor Game. Include a description of how you decide which move to make when it is your turn.

3. A Product Game board has this product grid.

4	6	8	9
12	16	18	24
27	32	36	48
54	64	72	?

   a. What factors would you need in order to play the game using this board?

   b. What product is missing?

4. Terrapin Crafts wants to rent between 30 and 50 square yards of space for a big crafts show. The space must be rectangular, and the side lengths must be whole numbers.

   a. Which number(s) of square yards, between 30 and 50, would give them the greatest number of rectangular arrangements to choose from?

   b. Which number(s) of square yards, between 30 and 50, would allow them to have a square space in which to set up their booth?

Check-Up 2

In 1–4, list all the factor pairs for each number.

1. 18

2. 25

3. 36

4. 48

In 5 and 6, list all the common factors for each pair of numbers.

5. 36 and 48

6. 25 and 36

In 7–10, list the first ten multiples of each number.

7. 18

8. 25

9. 36

10. 48

11. Use your lists from questions 9 and 10 to find the common multiples of 36 and 48.

12. Find a common multiple of 36 and 48 that is not in your lists.

In 13–15, write the prime factorization of each number.

13. 48

14. 95

15. 120

16. Jill says 6 is a common factor of 56 and 36. Is she correct? Explain your reasoning.

Quiz B

1. Vicente made three dozen cookies for the student council bake sale. He wants to package them in small bags with the same number of cookies in each bag.

   a. List all the ways Vicente can package the cookies.

   b. If you were Vicente, how many cookies would you put in each bag? Why?

   c. Vicente spent $5.40 on ingredients for the cookies. The student council will pay him back for the money he spent. For each of the answers you have for part a, determine how much the student council should charge for each bag of cookies so they make a profit yet still get students to buy the cookies.

2. Two radio stations are playing the number 1 hit song "2 Nice 2 B True" by Anita and the Goody-2-Shoes. WMTH plays the song every 18 minutes. WMSU plays the song every 24 minutes. Both stations play the song at 3:00 P.M.

   a. When is the next time the stations will play the song at the same time?

   b. When is the next time they will both play the song at the top of the hour?

3. List four pairs of numbers whose least common multiple is the same as their product. For example, the least common multiple of 5 and 6 is 30.

4. List four pairs of numbers whose least common multiple is smaller than their product. For example, the least common multiple of 6 and 9 is 18.

5. For a given pair of numbers, how can you tell whether the least common multiple will be less than or equal to their product?

6. Judith is planning a party for her younger brother. She has 36 prizes and 24 balloons. How many children can she have at the party so that each child gets an equal number of prizes and an equal number of balloons? Explain your answer.

Assign these questions as additional homework, or use them as review, quiz, or test questions.

1. Scarlett and Rhett were playing the Factor Game when Ashley looked over and saw that the numbers 1 to 15 were all circled. Ashley immediately said, "Oh, I see that your game is over." Is Ashley correct? Explain your answer.

In 2–4, describe how you can tell whether a given number is a multiple of the number shown.

2. 2   3. 3   4. 5

5. List all multiples of 6 between 1 and 100. What do these numbers have in common?

6. Mr. Matsumoto said, "I am thinking of a number. I know that to be sure I find all of the factor pairs of this number, I have to check all the numbers from 1 through 15."
    a. What is the smallest number he could be thinking of? Explain your answer.
    b. What is the largest number he could be thinking of? Explain your answer.

7. What is the mystery number?
    Clue 1 My number is between the square numbers 1 and 25.
    Clue 2 My number has exactly two factors.
    Clue 3 Both 66 and 605 are multiples of my number.

8. Use concepts you have learned in this unit to create a mystery number question. Each clue must contain at least one word from your vocabulary list.

9. a. List the first ten square numbers.
    b. Give all the factors for each number you listed in part a.
    c. Which of the square numbers you listed have only three factors?
    d. If you continued your list, what would be the next square number with only three factors?

10. A mystery number is greater than 50 and less than 100. You can make exactly five different rectangles with the mystery number of tiles. Its prime factorization consists of only one prime number. What is the number?

11. A number has 4 and 5 as factors.

   a. What other numbers must be factors? Explain your answer.

   b. What is the smallest the number could be?

12. Chairs for a meeting are arranged in six rows. Every row has the same number of chairs.

   a. What is the minimum possible number of chairs that could be in the room?

   b. If 100 is the maximum number of people allowed in the meeting room, what other numbers of chairs are possible?

13. Gloomy Toothpaste comes in two sizes: 9 ounces for $0.89 and 12 ounces for $1.15.

   a. Ben and Aaron bought the same amount of toothpaste. Ben bought only 9-ounce tubes, and Aaron bought only 12-ounce tubes. What is the smallest possible number of tubes each boy bought? (Hint: Use your knowledge of multiples to help you.)

   b. Which size tube is the better buy?

14. Circle the letter(s) of the statements that are always true about any prime number.

   a. It is divisible by only itself and 1.

   b. It is a factor of 1.

   c. It is divisible by another prime number.

   d. It is always an odd number.

15. Tyrone claims that the longest string of factors for 48 is $48 = 2 \times 2 \times 2 \times 2 \times 3$. Ian says there is a longer string. He wrote $48 = 1 \times 1 \times 1 \times 1 \times 1 \times 2 \times 2 \times 2 \times 2 \times 3$. Who is correct? Why?

16. What is the smallest number divisible by the first three prime numbers and the first three composite numbers? Explain how you got your answer.

Unit Test

1. Find three different ways to factor each of the following numbers into a product of factors. Do not use 1 as a factor.

   a. 72   b. 16

   c. 105   d. 132

2. A two-digit number that is less than 81 has 26 and 6 as factors. Find the number and explain your reasoning.

3. Fran has made a rectangle using 36 square tiles. The sum of the length and width of her rectangle is 15.

   a. What are the length and width of Fran's rectangle? Explain your reasoning.

   b. Would it be possible for the length and width of Fran's rectangle to be 11 and 4? Explain why or why not.

4. The diagrams below show three rectangles made from square tiles. Use the diagrams to answer each of the following questions.

   a. For each of the three rectangles, explain how the length and width of the rectangle are factors of the area of the rectangle.

   b. For each of the three rectangles, are the length and width the only factors of the area of the rectangle if you exclude a length or width of 1? Explain why or why not.

5. List all of the factor pairs for each of the following numbers.

    a. 48   **b.** 93   **c.** 32   **d.** 102

6. Find the dimensions of all of the rectangles that can be made with the same number of tiles as in the rectangle below. Explain how you found your answers.

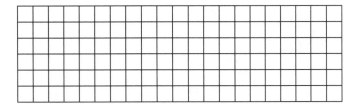

7. What number has the prime factorization $2^2 \times 3 \times 5^2 \times 7$? Explain your reasoning.

8. A number can be factored into the product $3^2 \times 9^3 \times 7^4$.

    a. Is the number even or odd? Explain your reasoning.

    b. Is the expression above the prime factorization of the number? Explain why or why not.

9. Marcia has developed a rule for generating a number sequence. The first 6 numbers in her sequence are 7, 21, 42, 126, 252, 756.

    a. What is Marcia's rule for finding the numbers in her sequence? Explain how you found your answer.

    b. What are the next two numbers in Marcia's sequence?

    c. What is the greatest common factor (GCF) of all the terms in Marcia's sequence? Explain your reasoning.

Name _____ Date _____

Notebook Checklist

Journal Organization

_____ Problems and Mathematical Reflections are labeled and dated.

_____ Work is neat and easy to find and follow.

Vocabulary

_____ All words are listed.   _____ All words are defined and described.

Quizzes and Check-Ups

_____ Quiz A   _____ Check-Up 1

_____ Quiz B   _____ Check-Up 2

Homework Assignments

_____ _____

_____ _____

_____ _____

_____ _____

_____ _____

_____ _____

_____ _____

_____ _____

_____ _____

_____ _____

_____ _____

_____ _____

_____ _____

_____ _____

Self-Assessment

Vocabulary

Of the vocabulary words I defined or described in my journal, the word _____ best demonstrates my ability to give a clear definition or description.

Of the vocabulary words I defined or described in my journal, the word _____ best demonstrates my ability to use an example to help explain or describe an idea.

Mathematical Ideas

1. a. I learned these things about numbers and their properties from *Prime Time:*

    b. Here are page numbers of journal entries that give evidence of what I have learned, along with descriptions of what each entry shows:

2. a. These are the mathematical ideas I am still struggling with:

    b. This is why I think these ideas are difficult for me:

    c. Here are page numbers of journal entries that give evidence of what I am struggling with, along with descriptions of what each entry shows:

Class Participation

I contributed to the classroom discussion and understanding of *Prime Time* when I…
(Give examples.)

Assessment Resources

for
Data About Us

Name _____ Date _____

1. Consider each distribution below. For each distribution, where possible, tell how many people are represented by the data, and identify the mode, median, and range.

   a.

   Lengths of Last Names

   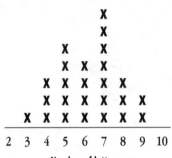

   Number of letters

   b.

   Lengths of Last Names

   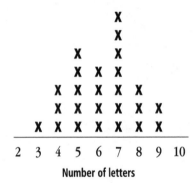

   Number of letters

2. On the back of this page, make a line plot showing the lengths of 11 names so that the median length is 12 letters and the range is from 6 letters to 16 letters.

3. The media specialist in your school is planning a book fair. She is preparing a survey to ask students a few questions to help make the book fair a success.
   a. Write one question that will give the media specialist *numerical* data.

   b. Write one question that will give the media specialist *categorical* data.

Quiz

Questions 1–3 explore the question of what time a typical student goes to bed on a school night. Your teacher will share your class's data on bedtimes with you. Use this data for the following questions.

1. Organize and display your class's data on bedtimes using an appropriate graph.

2. Answer the following questions about your class's data.
    a. What is the range of the data?

    b. What is the mode of the data? How many students had a bedtime the same as the mode?

    c. What is the median of the data? How many students had a bedtime the same as the median?

    d. Are there any outliers in the data? If so, what might cause this?

3. Based on the class's data, what would you say is the typical time a student in your class goes to bed on a school night? Explain your reasoning.

Quiz

4. A group of students were curious about the changes in people's height over time. They gathered data about height from two different groups of students in their district: students in grade 5 and students in grade 8. The data they collected is shown in the table.

   a. Make stem-and-leaf plots that show these data.

   b. What is the typical height of the grade 5 students? Justify your answer.

   c. What is the typical height of the grade 8 students? Justify your answer.

   d. How does the height data from the grade 5 class compare with the height data from the grade 8 class?

   e. There were three grade 8 students absent the day the data were collected. Their heights are 177 cm, 187 cm, and 163 cm. What happens to the mean, mode, and median when these new values are added to the data set?

Height (centimeters)	
Grade 5	Grade 8
138	147
138	156
138	159
139	160
141	160
142	161
144	162
146	162
147	162
147	162
147	163
150	164
150	165
151	165
151	168
151	168
151	168
152	168
152	169
152	171
152	172
153	174
153	176
155	
155	
156	
156	
157	
158	
171	

Quiz

5. Two students went to a frog-jumping contest. They wondered whether there might be a relationship between a frog's weight and its jumping ability. The biology teacher had frogs in her lab, and the two students decided to investigate their question: "What is the relationship between a frog's weight and how far it jumps?" They collected the data on the right from the 26 frogs in the science lab.

a. On another sheet of paper, make a coordinate graph that shows each frog's weight and the length of its jump. Put weight measurements on the *x*-axis (the horizontal axis) and length measurements on the *y*-axis (the vertical axis).

b. Describe any patterns in the graph.

c. What can you say about the relationship between the weight of a frog in this group and the length of its jump?

d. What is the median weight of the frogs?

e. What is the median jump of the frogs?

f. How many frogs have a weight above the median weight and a jump above the median jump?

g. How many frogs have a weight above the median weight and a jump below the median jump?

Frog Data

Name of frog	Weight (grams)	Length of jump (centimeters)
Jumper	70	43
Webster	100	64
Leapy Leo	80	32
Kroaker	120	46
Fruity	100	37
Frogzilla	120	46
Jalapeño	100	28
Big Bertha	70	52
Tommy	90	34.5
Thunder	140	49.5
Kirby	120	35.5
Sliminator	120	30
Horton	90	26
Kekokekory	100	29
Pippin	130	52
Speedy	110	26.5
Lightning	80	32
Coco	135	32
Fast Freddie	120	27.5
Jumpfaster	100	26
Terminator	130	26
Froggy	100	54
Kickin'	130	49
Sir Kermit	130	30
Bullet	130	34
Nimrod	65	28.5

Assign these questions as additional homework, or use them as review, quiz, or test questions.

1. For the distribution below, tell how many people are represented and identify the mode, median, and range.

Lengths of First Names

```
X
X  X
X  X  X
X  X  X  X
_____
3  4  5  6  7  8
```
Number of letters

2. Suppose you wanted to describe the typical student in your grade. You decide to design a survey to help collect information about students in your grade.
   a. Write one question for your survey that will give you *numerical* data. Explain how this information would help you to describe the typical student.

   b. Write one question for your survey that will give you *categorical* data. Explain how this information would help you to describe the typical student.

3. Make a line plot showing the ages in years of 12 students so that the median age is 12.5 years and the difference between the highest age and the lowest age is 9 years.

4. The mean number of children in six families is 5 children.
   a. What is the total number of children in the six families?
   b. Other than six families of 5 children, create a set of families that fits this information.
   c. Would another classmate's set of families for question b have to be the same as yours? Explain.

5. In the story *The Phantom Tollbooth*, Milo is told that the average number of children in a family is 2.58. You know that a .58 boy or girl cannot exist. How could the calculations for the mean produce this number?

6. Most people will walk about 158,125 kilometers in their lifetime, or around the world 4.5 times.

   a. How do you suppose this statistic was determined?

   b. What might you do if you were asked to investigate the question, How far do most people walk in their lifetime?

7. A class investigated how many pets each student in the class had. A number of students in their class had no pets at all. Here's how their data looked:

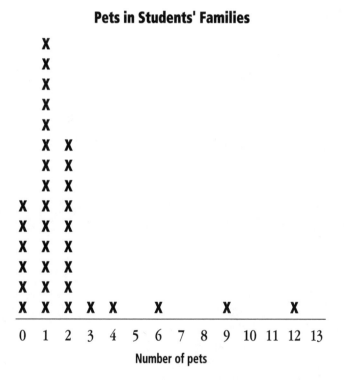

Pets in Students' Families

Number of pets

   a. Would it be possible to have a data set for which the median number of pets for students is 0? Explain.

   b. Would it be possible to have a data set for which the mean number of pets for students is 0? Explain.

Unit Test

1. A group of 9 students has these numbers of children in their families: 3, 2, 4, 2, 1, 5, 1, 2, and 7.
   a. Find the median number of children in the 9 families.

   b. Find the mean number of children in the 9 families.

2. The stem plot below shows test scores for Ms. McIntyre's class on a state mathematics test. Students could score from 0 to 100 points.

Class Test Scores

```
0 | 5
1 |
2 | 4
3 | 4 9
4 | 3 7 8
5 | 7 9
6 | 1 6 8
7 | 3 5 6 8 8
8 | 1 2 2 2 5
9 | 0 3 9
```

   a. Are these data numerical or categorical?

   b. What is the range of the data?

   c. What is the median of the data? How many students had a score the same as the median?

Unit Test

3. Fourteen students read the book *Gulliver's Travels*. In the book, the Lilliputians said they could make clothes for Gulliver by taking one measurement, the length around his thumb. The Lilliputians claimed that

• the distance around Gulliver's wrist would be twice the distance around his thumb.

• the distance around Gulliver's neck would be twice the distance around his wrist.

• the distance around Gulliver's waist would be twice the distance around his neck.

The students wondered whether this doubling relationship would be true for them too. They measured the distance around their thumbs and their wrists in centimeters, then graphed the pairs of numbers on a coordinate graph. They drew a line connecting the points that represented wrist measurements that were twice thumb measurements.

Thumb and Wrist Measurements

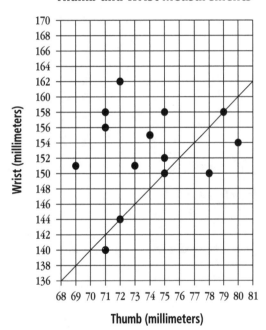

a. How many students' measurements fit the Lilliputian rule that twice the distance around the thumb equals the distance around the wrist?

b. How many students' wrist measurements are less than twice their thumb measurements?

Unit Test

c. The point for Jeri's thumb and wrist measurements is above the line. If the cuffs of a shirt are twice the measurement around Jeri's thumb, how will the cuffs of the shirt fit her?

d. The point for Rubin's thumb and wrist measurements is below the line. If the cuffs of a shirt are twice the measurement around Rubin's thumb, how will the cuffs of the shirt fit him?

4. A class investigated the question of how many paces it takes to travel from their class to the gym. They measured the distance by counting the number of paces each student walked. Every step made on the right foot counted as one pace. Here are their results:

Paces to the Gym

```
                    X
                    X
                    X   X
                    X   X
            X       X   X   X
    X       X   X   X   X   X   X
    X   X   X   X   X   X   X   X
    _____
    16  17  18  19  20  21  22  23  24  25  26
```

a. What is the median number of paces the students took to travel the distance?

b. Make a bar graph that displays this information. Explain how the bar graph is similar to and different from a line plot.

c. Who has the shorter pace: the student who traveled the distance in 17 paces or the student who traveled the distance in 25 paces? Explain your reasoning.

Name _____ Date _____

Journal Organization

—— Problems and Mathematical Reflections are labeled and dated.

—— Work is neat and easy to find and follow.

Vocabulary

—— All words are listed.

—— All words are defined or described.

Check-Up and Quiz

—— Check-Up   —— Quiz

Homework Assignments

—— _____

—— _____

—— _____

—— _____

—— _____

—— _____

—— _____

—— _____

—— _____

—— _____

—— _____

—— _____

—— _____

Self-Assessment

Vocabulary

Of the vocabulary words I defined or described in my journal, the word _____ best demonstrates my ability to give a clear definition or description.

Of the vocabulary words I defined or described in my journal, the word _____ best demonstrates my ability to use an example to help explain or describe an idea.

Mathematical Ideas

1. **a.** I learned these things about collecting, displaying, and analyzing data from *Data About Us:*

    b. Here are page numbers of journal entries that give evidence of what I have learned, along with descriptions of what each entry shows:

2. **a.** These are the mathematical ideas I am still struggling with:

    b. This is why I think these ideas are difficult for me:

    c. Here are page numbers of journal entries that give evidence of what I am struggling with, along with descriptions of what each entry shows:

Class Participation

I contributed to the classroom discussion and understanding of *Data About Us* when I . . .
(Give examples.)

Assessment Resources

for
Shapes and Designs

Check-Up 1

In 1–5, decide whether the given statement is true or false. Give explanations or sketches to support your answers.

1. With side lengths 6, 8, and 10, there is one and only one triangle shape that can be made.

2. Any two quadrilaterals that have sides of the same lengths will be identical in size and shape. For example, two quadrilaterals with side lengths 5, 7, 9, and 11 will be the same size and shape.

3. There can be no pentagon with sides lengths 2, 2, 3, 7, and 15.

4. All rectangles are special kinds of parallelograms.

5. All parallelograms are special kinds of squares.

In 6–8, use an angle ruler to measure each angle.

6.

7.

8.

Check-Up 1

In 9 and 10, draw an angle with the given measure.

9. 90°

10. 150°

One of the most common places we see angles is on the faces of clocks. At the start of each hour, the minute hand is pointed straight up, at the 12. In 11–13, mark where the minute hand is at the start of an hour as one side of an angle. Sketch the angle formed by the minute hand at the time shown, and give the measure of the angle.

11. 10 minutes

12. 45 minutes

13. 25 minutes

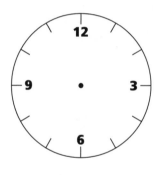

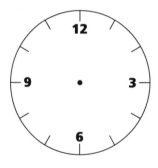

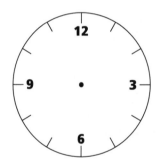

angle = _____

angle = _____

angle = _____

Check-Up 2

In 1–4, decide whether the given statements are true or false. Give explanations or sketches to support your answers.

1. You can always completely surround a point by placing the vertices of four squares together.

2. The sum of the measures of the angles of any triangle is 90°.

3. In a regular hexagon, all sides are the same length and all angles are 100°.

4. Any triangle can be used to tile a flat surface.

5. Use shapes A, B, C, D, E, or F from your Shapes Set to answer a–c.
   a. Choose a single shape and show how it tiles.

   b. Choose a single shape and show how it does not tile.

Check-Up 2

c. Explain why the one shape you chose did tile and the other shape you chose did not tile.

In 6–9, use the given data and what you know about relations among sides and angles to find the lengths and angle measurements of all sides and angles in the figures.

6. square

2 cm

7. rectangle

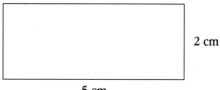

2 cm

5 cm

8. parallelogram

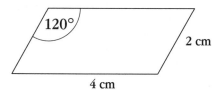

120°

2 cm

4 cm

9. parallelogram

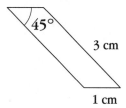

45°

3 cm

1 cm

Name _____ Date _____

Below is the face of a compass. It is standard practice to match each compass direction with the degree measure of the angle formed by a clockwise turn from due north (N) to the desired direction. For example, east (E) is given the direction number 90°.

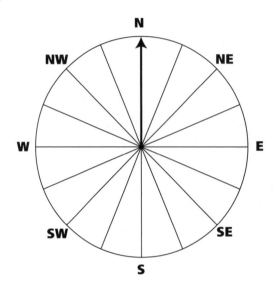

In 1–8, find the direction number for the given point of the compass.

1. NE (northeast)

2. SE (southeast)

3. S (south)

4. SW (southwest)

5. W (west)

6. NW (northwest)

7. N (north)

8. NNE (north-northeast, between N and NE)

In 9 and 10, show all the line symmetries and give the degree measures for all the turn symmetries for the given shape from your Shapes Set.

9. shape C

10. shape K

11. Jack has made a tiling with quadrilateral shapes. Jack can pick up a shape from his tiling and turn it 90°, and it will fit back where it was. Kenesha has used a different quadrilateral to make a tiling. Kenesha's quadrilateral will not fit back into the pattern when she turns it 90°.

   a. What might Jack's quadrilateral look like? Draw or describe it, and explain why it works.

   b. What might Kenesha's quadrilateral look like? Draw or describe it, and explain why it doesn't fit back into the tiling pattern when it is turned 90°.

Quiz

In 12 and 13, given the computer code, what figure will be drawn?

12. fd 25
    rt 120
    fd 25
    rt 120
    fd 25

13. rt 60
    fd 100
    rt 90
    fd 100
    rt 90
    fd 100
    rt 90
    fd 100

In 14–17, use the shapes on the following page.

14. The figures I, L, and V can be grouped together, but X would not belong in the group. Explain why.

15. The figures E, G, H, I, and M can be grouped together, but S would not belong in the group. Explain why.

16. The figures F, Q, W, and X can be grouped together, but N would not belong in the group. Explain why.

17. The figures A, B, H, J, M, S, and U can be grouped together, but N would not belong in the group. Explain why.

Quiz

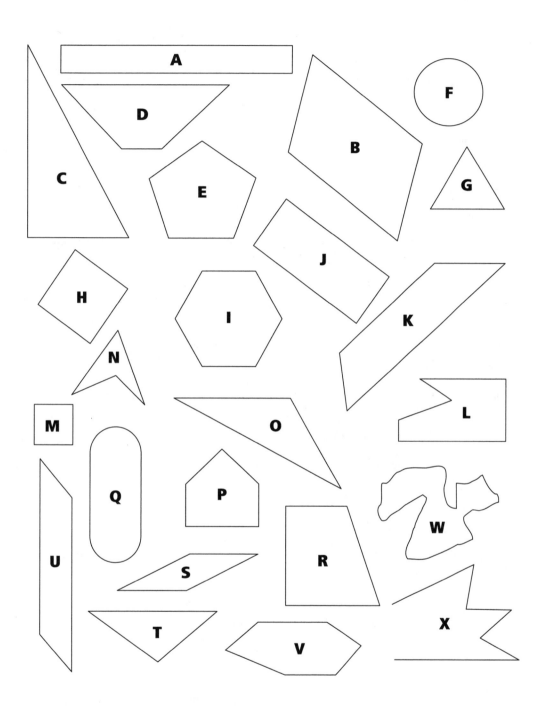

Assign these questions as additional homework, or use them as review, quiz, or test questions.

1. Spread your fingers and look at the angles created by them. In a–c, use your angle ruler to measure the angles formed by the given fingers. (To take the measure, lay your hand flat on your desk and spread the fingers you are measuring as far as possible.)

   a. Your thumb and first finger

   b. Your index and middle finger

   c. Your thumb and pinkie finger

   d. How do your measurements for a, b, and c compare?

2. Naomi picked 3, 6, 6, and 12 for the side lengths of a quadrilateral. Marcelo says she cannot make a quadrilateral with these lengths. Is he right? Explain.

In 3–5, decide whether the given statement is true or false. Give explanations or sketches to support your answers.

3. A quadrilateral with sides 5, 8, 5, 8, in that order, is always a rectangle.

4. A quadrilateral with two sides of 7 and two sides of 11 is always a parallelogram.

5. You will always be able to draw two different triangles using side lengths of 3, 4, and 5.

In 6–8, use a coordinate grid like the one shown below.

6. If a line segment connecting (4, 3) and (7, 6) forms one *side* of a square, what might be the coordinates of the other corners of that square?

7. If (2, 0) and (5, 5) are two vertices of a triangle that does not have a right angle, what might be the coordinates of the other vertex of that triangle?

8. Draw your triangle for question 7. For each angle of the triangle, tell whether the angles are greater than or less than 90°.

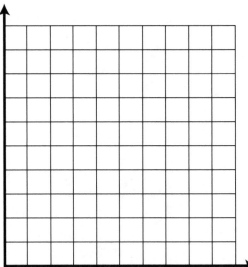

9. Alejandro's dad bought pentagon tiles to tile his patio. When he returned with the tiles and showed them to Alejandro, Alejandro told him that he would have to go back for another shape tile to go with the pentagon tiles or exchange the pentagon tiles for a different shape altogether, because the pentagon alone would not work to tile the patio. Was Alejandro correct? Why or why not?

10. G. Oni Ometer is a math rap singer who lives in Miami, Florida. She is starting a fall concert tour, and she flies her own plane to every concert. Here is her tour schedule:

Dallas, Texas	September 14–16
Boston, Massachusetts	September 18–20
San Diego, California	September 22–25
Detroit, Michigan	September 27–30
Miami, Florida	October 2–8

To fly from one city to the next, G. Oni needs a flight angle and compass direction to direct her plane. A flight angle is formed by a two lines that start in the city from which the flight takes off. One line points north, and the other points to the flight's destination. The flight angles are labeled with degree measure and west or east. For example, to fly from Miami to Dallas for the first concert, G. Oni flies along a 71° west flight angle. Using your angle ruler and the map below, find the flight angles for the rest of G. Oni's concert tour.

Unit Test

1. **a.** Is the triangle at the right a regular polygon? Explain why or why not.

    b. Could this triangle be used to tile a surface? Explain why or why not.

2. An equilateral triangle has a perimeter of 12. What is the length of each side? Explain your reasoning.

3. A square has a perimeter of 16.4 centimeters. What is the length of each side? Explain your reasoning

4. For each of the shapes below, find the unknown angle measure without using your angle ruler.

    a.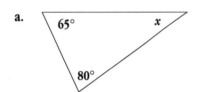
    b.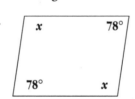
    c.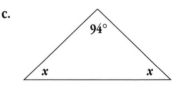

5. Is it possible for a parallelogram to have a 54° angle and a 126° angle? Explain why or why not.

    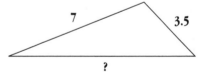

6. Use the triangle at right to answer the following questions.

    a. Ted estimates that the unknown side length is 11. How do you think his estimate compares with the actual length? Explain your reasoning.

    b. Felicia estimates that the unknown side length is 6.75. How do you think her estimate compares with the actual length? Explain your reasoning.

    c. Make your own estimate of the unknown side length. Explain your strategy for finding your estimate, and explain why you think your estimate is reasonable.

7. A rectangle has a perimeter of 42 centimeters. One of its sides is 11 centimeters long. What are the dimensions of the rectangle? Explain your answer.

8. Is it possible for a triangle to have angles with measures 34°, 45°, and 100°?

9. In the diagram below, what are the measures of the five angles?

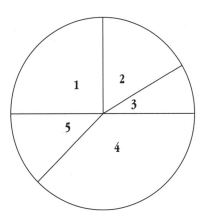

10. Refer to the Logo program to answer the following questions.

```
rt 30
fd 90
rt 60
fd 120
rt 120
fd 90
rt 60
fd 120
```

   a. If you run this program, what kind of figure will it draw?

   b. What is the sum of the side lengths of the figure in turtle steps?

   c. What are the measures of the angles of the figure?

Notebook Checklist

Journal Organization

_____ Problems and Mathematical Reflections are labeled and dated.

_____ Work is neat and easy to find and follow.

Vocabulary

_____ All words are listed.

_____ All words are defined or described.

Quizzes and Check-Ups

_____ Quiz _____ Check-Up 1 _____ Check-Up 2

Homework Assignments

_____ _____

_____ _____

_____ _____

_____ _____

_____ _____

_____ _____

_____ _____

_____ _____

_____ _____

_____ _____

_____ _____

_____ _____

_____ _____

_____ _____

_____ _____

_____ _____

Self-Assessment

Vocabulary

Of the vocabulary words I defined or described in my journal, the word _____ best demonstrates my ability to give a clear definition or description.

Of the vocabulary words I defined or described in my journal, the word _____ best demonstrates my ability to use an example to help explain or describe an idea.

Mathematical Ideas

1. a. I learned these things about how sides and angles form shapes of polygons:

    b. Here are page numbers of journal entries that give evidence of what I have learned, along with descriptions of what each entry shows:

2. a. These are the mathematical ideas I am still struggling with:

    b. This is why I think these ideas are difficult for me:

    c. Here are page numbers of journal entries that give evidence of what I am struggling with, along with descriptions of what each entry shows:

Class Participation

I contributed to the classroom discussion and understanding of *Shapes and Designs* when I...
(Give examples.)

Assessment Resources

for
Bits and Pieces I

Name _____ Date _____

1. This sketch shows part of a ruler. The main marks indicate inches.

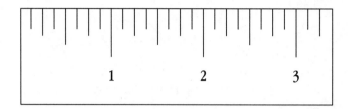

   How do you think each of the marks between the inches should be labeled? Explain your answer.

2. Use your fraction strips or another method to compare the two fractions in each pair. Insert the correct sign:
   <, >, or =.

   a. $\frac{8}{12}$ $\frac{3}{4}$ b. $\frac{5}{8}$ $\frac{6}{10}$ c. $\frac{2}{3}$ $\frac{5}{6}$ d. $\frac{2}{4}$ $\frac{7}{12}$ e. $\frac{3}{8}$ $\frac{3}{12}$

3. Find three different fractions between the benchmarks $\frac{1}{2}$ and $\frac{3}{4}$.

Check-Up 1

4. Julie's math class and Dave's math class are selling sub sandwiches as a fund-raiser. Each class has a goal of $150. Julie said her class was closer to the goal than Dave's class because her class had earned $\frac{2}{3}$ of their goal, and Dave's class had earned $\frac{5}{8}$ of their goal. Was Julie right? Explain your answer.

5. Estimate and mark where the number 1 will be on each number line. The length that represents the whole may be different on each number line.

   a.

   $0 \qquad \frac{1}{6}$

   b.

   $0 \qquad\qquad \frac{3}{4}$

   c.

   $0 \qquad\qquad\qquad \frac{3}{2}$

6. Order these numbers from smallest to largest:

   $1\frac{7}{10} \qquad 1\frac{15}{18} \qquad \frac{24}{15}$

Quiz

1. Give a fraction name for the shaded part of the figure below. Explain how you figured out what fractional part of the whole was shaded.

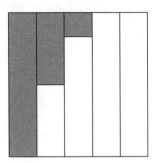

2. Lynette found a worm that is $\frac{2}{3}$ of the length of your fraction strip. How many worms exactly like hers would you need to put end to end to equal two times the length of your fraction strip? Explain your answer.

3. Decide whether each of the following statements is true or false, and explain why:

   a. If you compare two fractions with the same denominator, the fraction with the greater numerator is greater.

   b. If you compare two fractions with the same numerator, the fraction with the greater denominator is greater.

Quiz

4. Antonio's father agreed to help with an Events Night at camp by setting up a pizza stand to sell pizza to visiting family and friends. Antonio's father has only one size of pizza pan, a circular pan with a 16-inch diameter. The class committee decided they wanted him to sell pizza by the slice and to sell small slices and large slices. Antonio's father has a cutting form that can cut a pizza into 12 slices and another form that can cut a pizza into 8 slices.

   a. If a family bought three small slices and three large slices, what fraction of a pizza did they buy? (You might want to draw a picture to help you.)

   b. How much more pizza (what fraction) would they need to buy to purchase a whole pizza?

   c. How many different ways can you combine small slices and large slices to make a whole pizza? Write each of your responses as number sentences. For example: $\frac{2}{8} + \frac{9}{12} = 1$ means that two large slices and nine small slices will make one whole pizza.

5. In each pair of pencils, the length of the unused pencil is about what fraction of the length of the sharpened pencil?

   a.

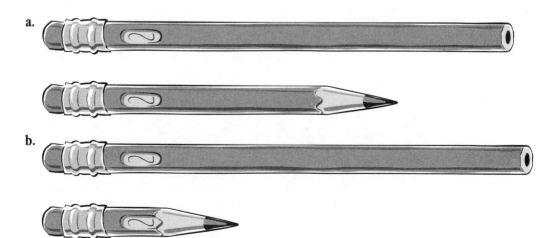

   b.

Check-Up 2

1. For each figure below, give a fraction name and a decimal name for the shaded part.

    a.

    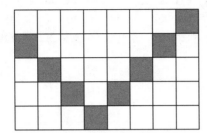

    b.

    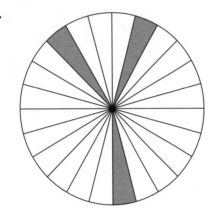

2. Arrange these decimals in order from smallest to largest:

    6.00   0.6   0.006   0.60   0.06   0.00006

Check-Up 2

3. On each figure below, shade the indicated decimal amount.

   a. 0.375

   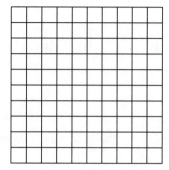

   b. 0.6

   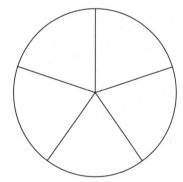

   c. 0.05

   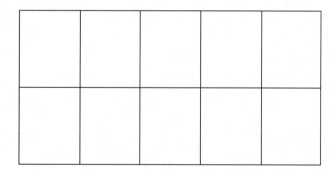

4. Rename each of the decimal amounts in question 3 with fraction names.

   a. _____   b. _____   c. _____

Check-Up 2

5. On the strip below, mark and label where each of these decimals is: 0.09, 0.9, 0.19, 0.190, 0.019.

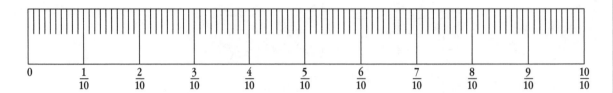

6. For each number line, fill in the missing decimal numbers. For example, filling in the missing decimal numbers on this number line:

0.019   0.023

would give you this:

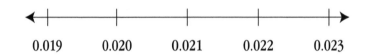

0.019   0.020   0.021   0.022   0.023

a.

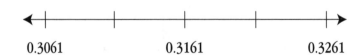

0.01   0.03

b.

0.3061   0.3161   0.3261

c.

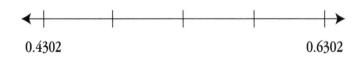

0.4302   0.6302

Assign these questions as additional homework, or use them as review, quiz, or test questions.

1. This is a carnival game that tests strength. The player
    hits the block with a mallet and the force of the blow
    sends a metal ringer up the pole. If the player uses
    enough force, the ringer rings the bell at the top of the
    pole and the player receives the top prize of 100
    points. The player receives fewer points for hits that
    send the metal ringer only partway up the pole. The
    points can be traded for tickets to rides at the carnival.

    a. Where should marks be made on the pole for
        each of the game point amounts? Mark them on
        the pole.

10 points	25 points	35 points
70 points	85 points	100 points

    b. What fraction of the pole would each of the
        marks in part a represent?

    c. What payoff, in game points, should
        be given for sending the metal ringer
        $\frac{1}{3}$ of the way up the pole?

    d. What payoff, in game points, should be given for sending the ringer $\frac{3}{5}$ of the way up the pole?

    e. What payoff, in game points, should be given for sending the ringer $\frac{2}{8}$ of the way up the pole?

    f. What payoff, in game points, should be given for sending the ringer $\frac{3}{4}$ of the way up the pole?

    g. Miki's hit sent the metal ringer $\frac{5}{8}$ of the way up the pole. Taylor's hit went $\frac{6}{9}$ of the way to the top. Who
        received the most game points? Why?

2. You are invited to go out for pizza with several friends. When you get there, your friends are sitting in two separate groups. You can join either group. If you join the first group, there will be a total of 4 people in the group and you will be sharing 6 small pizzas. If you join the second group, there will be a total of 6 people in the group and you will be sharing 8 small pizzas. If pizza will be shared equally in each group—and you are *very* hungry—which would you rather join? Explain your choice.

3. a. Three is what fractional part of 12?

   b. Five is what fractional part of 20?

   c. Two is what fractional part of 9?

   d. Seven is what fractional part of 17?

4. Samuel is getting a snack for himself and his little brother. There are two muffins in the refrigerator. Samuel takes half of one muffin for himself and half of the other muffin for his little brother. His little brother complains that Samuel got more. Samuel says that he got $\frac{1}{2}$ and his brother got $\frac{1}{2}$. What might be the problem?

5. Your best friend was absent when your class learned how to compare decimal numbers. Write a set of directions that would help your friend understand how to compare decimal numbers.

6. The following prices were posted at a local store.

Bananas .39¢ a pound

Notebook Paper 1.02¢

What is wrong with these signs?

7. Use these numbers to fill in the blanks so that the story makes numerical sense:

   645     $\frac{3}{4}$ 65   215   75   161.25   35 $\frac{1}{4}$ 330.65

   Events Night a Huge Success!

   The Events Night held by Mr. Martinez's and Ms. Swanson's middle-school classes was a success, raising a total of $_____ . The teachers estimated the large turnout of middle-school students included over_____ of the building's student population. Over half of the money, $_____ , was earned by the food booths. _____ game tickets were sold, raising $_____ , which represented_____ of the money. The tickets were_____ cents each. Most of the money that was raised, _____ %, will go toward paying for the class camping trip, and the other _____ % will be used to pay expenses.

8. In each of the sets of numbers below, one number is not equivalent to the others. Tell which one is not like the others and explain why.

   a. 0.60   0.6   6%

   b. $\frac{1}{25}$ 25%   0.25

   c. 0.75   34% $\frac{3}{4}$

9. Write a benchmark fraction that is close to each of these percentages:

   a. 23.6%   b. 45.4545%

Unit Test: In-Class Portion

1. In each figure, express the area shaded and the area not shaded as percents.

   a. 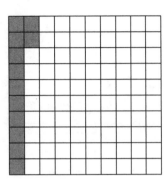   b. 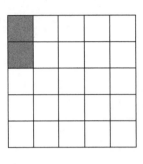   c.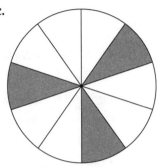

   % shaded _____   % shaded _____   % shaded _____

   % not shaded _____   % not shaded _____   % not shaded _____

2. Write each of the following as a fraction, decimal, and percent.

   a. 30 days out of 100 days   b. 55¢ compared to 100¢

   c. 20 correct out of 25 problems   d. 3 out of 4 games won

   e. 21 mountain bikes out of 40 bikes   f. 5 misspelled words out of 30 words

3. At the pizza shop, 16-inch-diameter pizzas sell for $9.85. The shop has decided to sell pizza by the slice. One cutting form can cut a pizza into 12 slices, and another form can cut a pizza into 8 slices.

   a. To make at least $9.85 on each whole pizza sold, how much should the shop charge for a large slice? (Try to come as close to $9.85 as you can, but make your price easy to handle in terms of making change.)

Unit Test: In-Class Portion

b. To make at least $9.85 on each whole pizza sold, how much should the shop charge for a small slice? (Try to come as close to $9.85 as you can, but make your price easy to handle.)

c. Explain why you think your answers for parts a and b are appropriate.

4. In a recent survey of 600 people, 20% said chocolate chip cookie was their favorite ice cream. How many people in the survey favored chocolate chip cookie ice cream? Explain your answer.

5. Of the people in your math class today (including your teacher), what percent are male? _____

What percent are female? _____

Unit Test: Individual Research

Find two different articles in newspapers or magazines that contain fractions, decimals, or percents. If one article uses mainly one of these forms, the other article must contain at least one of the other two forms.

Write a one- to two-paragraph summary of each article. In your explanation, tell how rational numbers were used in the article and what they represent. Turn in each article with your explanation attached.

Notebook Checklist

Journal Organization

_____ Problems and Mathematical Reflections are labeled and dated.

_____ Work is neat and easy to find and follow.

Vocabulary

_____ All words are listed.   _____ All words are defined and described.

Quizzes and Check-Ups

_____ Quiz   _____ Check-Up 1

               _____ Check-Up 2

Homework Assignments

_____ _____

_____ _____

_____ _____

_____ _____

_____ _____

_____ _____

_____ _____

_____ _____

_____ _____

_____ _____

_____ _____

_____ _____

_____ _____

_____ _____

Name _____ Date _____

Self-Assessment

Vocabulary

Of the vocabulary words I defined or described in my journal, the word _____ best demonstrates my ability to give a clear definition or description.

Of the vocabulary words I defined or described in my journal, the word _____ best demonstrates my ability to use an example to help explain or describe an idea.

Mathematical Ideas

1. a. I learned these things about fractions, decimals, and percents in *Bits and Pieces I*:

    b. Here are page numbers of journal entries that give evidence of what I have learned, along with descriptions of what each entry shows:

2. a. These are the mathematical ideas I am still struggling with:

    b. This is why I think these ideas are difficult for me:

    c. Here are page numbers of journal entries that give evidence of what I am struggling with, along with descriptions of what each entry shows:

Class Participation

I contributed to the classroom discussion and understanding of *Bits and Pieces I* when I . . .
(Give examples.)

Assessment Resources

for
*Covering and
Surrounding*

Check-Up 1

1. The squares on this grid are 1 centimeter long and 1 centimeter wide. Outline two different figures with an area of 12 square centimeters and a perimeter of 16 centimeters.

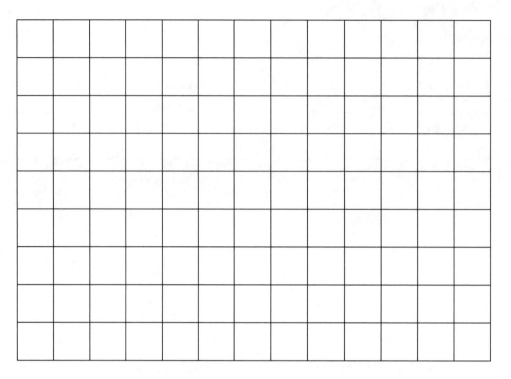

2. **a.** On grid paper, sketch all the rectangles that can be made from exactly 16 square tiles.
   b. What do all of your rectangles have in common?

   c. How are your rectangles different?

3. **a.** On grid paper, sketch all the rectangles with a perimeter of 16 units that can be made from square tiles.
   b. What do all of your rectangles have in common?

   c. How are your rectangles different? Explain.

4. Are the rectangles you sketched in questions 2 and 3 the same or different? Explain your answer.

Quiz A

1. Angela works as an intern with the Department of National Resources. She is working on a study of the wildlife in a marsh near San Francisco Bay. Angela has to figure out how the marsh has changed from 1990 to 1995. Statistics are computed on the marsh every 5 years. Here are aerial maps of the marsh in 1990 and in 1995.

Marsh in 1990

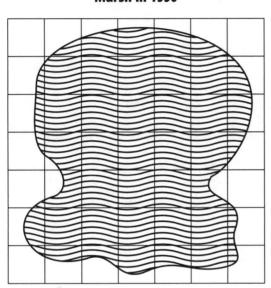

Marsh in 1995

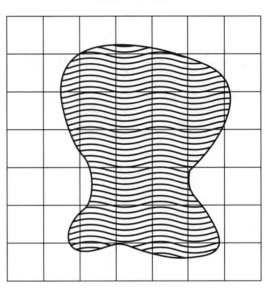

Scale

——— 1 mile

a. Find the approximate area and perimeter of the marsh in 1990 and in 1995.

1990 area: _____   1995 area: _____

1990 perimeter: _____   1995 perimeter: _____

b. Describe your methods for determining the area measurements in part a.

c. Do you think your estimates are too high or two low? Explain.

d. Try to imagine what may have caused changes in the marsh over the 5 years. Record your ideas.

Quiz A

2. Suppose you built all the rectangles possible from 48 square tiles.
   a. Describe the rectangle that would have the largest perimeter.

   Dimensions: _____ Perimeter: _____

   b. Describe the rectangle that would have the smallest perimeter.

   Dimensions: _____ Perimeter: _____

3. Suppose you used square tiles to build all the rectangles possible with a perimeter of 48 units.
   a. Describe the rectangle that would have the largest area.

   Dimensions: _____ Area: _____

   b. Describe the rectangle that would have the smallest area.

   Dimensions: _____ Area: _____

4. Houses, trailers, and apartments come in many different sizes and shapes. On grid paper, design a floor plan, complete with window and door locations, that covers 800 square feet. Your plan should represent a reasonable use of space for a house, apartment, or trailer. Mark on your plan the inside walls that separate the rooms. Make an organized list of all the rooms, giving their purpose, dimensions, and area.

Check-Up 2

In 1–5, calculate the area and perimeter of the figure.

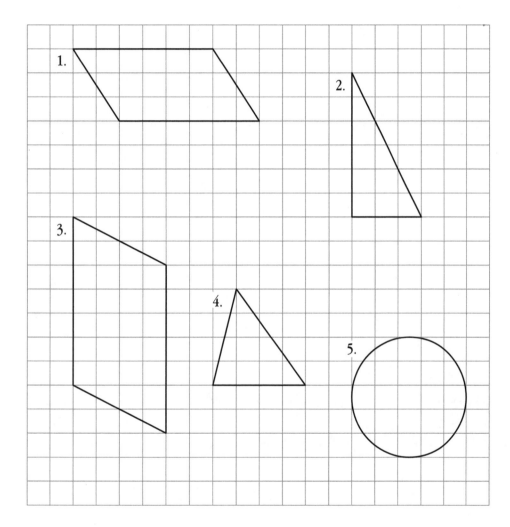

Check-Up 2

In 6–8, use what you learned in this unit to determine the area of the figure in square centimeters.

6.

7.

8.

9. You and two friends decide to go to the Pizza Nook for dinner. They have the best cheese pizzas in the neighborhood.

Pizza Nook Cheese Pizzas	
6-inch round pizza	$3.00
12-inch round pizza	$8.00
18-inch round pizza	$12.00

a. If you buy a 6-inch pizza, how many square inches of pizza will you get?

b. If you buy a 12-inch pizza, how many square inches of pizza will you get?

c. If you buy an 18-inch pizza, how many square inches of pizza will you get?

Quiz B

1. You may recall that the Pizza Nook sells great cheese pizzas for the following prices.

Pizza Nook Cheese Pizzas	
6-inch round pizza	$3.00
12-inch round pizza	$8.00
18-inch round pizza	$12.00

   a. How many 6-inch pizzas contain the same amount of pizza as one 12-inch pizza?

   b. How many 6-inch pizzas contain the same amount of pizza as one 18-inch pizza?

   c. The new manager of the Pizza Nook is thinking about changing the prices of cheese pizzas. It appears to him that he could think about the pricing in three ways:

   Method 1: The price of a pizza could be based on its diameter.
   Method 2: The price of a pizza could be based on its circumference.
   Method 3: The price of a pizza could be based on its area.

   If you were the manager, which method would you use to price the pizzas? Explain your reasoning.

Quiz B

2. Consider the following figures.

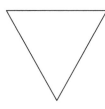 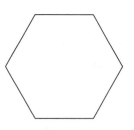 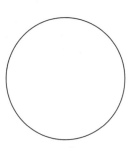

regular triangle
(equilateral triangle)　　regular quadrilateral
(square)　　regular hexagon　　circle

Suppose each figure has a perimeter of 24 centimeters.

a. What is the length of the edges for each polygon?

Triangle: _____

Quadrilateral: _____

Hexagon: _____

b. What is the diameter of the circle?

c. Which figure has the greatest area? Explain how you arrived at your answer.

Assign these questions as additional homework, or use them as review, quiz, or test questions. Grid paper, tiles, and transparent grids can be used as needed.

1. Jason is planning to redecorate his bedroom. He measured the room and made this rough sketch.

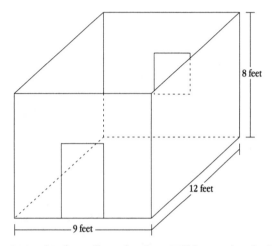

8 feet

12 feet

9 feet

a. Jason is planning to buy paint for the walls and ceiling. Will he need to find perimeter or area to figure out how much paint to buy? What unit of measure should he use?

b. To determine how much new carpet to buy, will Jason need to find perimeter or area? What unit of measure should he use?

c. Jason also needs baseboard for around the bottom of the walls. Will he need to find perimeter or area to figure out how much baseboard to buy? What unit of measure should he use?

d. How much carpeting does Jason need? Show how you found your answer.

e. How much baseboard does Jason need? Show how you found your answer.

f. If a gallon of paint covers 350 square feet, how much paint does Jason need for the walls and ceiling?

2. Chad's dad wants to repaint the top of the step outside the front door with special paint that doesn't get slippery in the rain. Below is a drawing of the top of the step. Each centimeter represents 1 foot.

3 cm

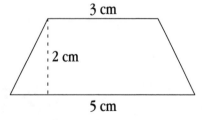

2 cm

5 cm

a. Using the scale drawing, help Chad's dad by finding the area of the step. Keep a record of your work and sketches so you can convince him that you found it correctly.

b. Each quart of paint covers 32 square feet. Chad's dad wants to apply two coats of paint. How many quarts of paint should he buy? Explain your answer.

3. Lydia's stepmother decided to paint the semicircular patio in their back yard. Here is Lydia's sketch of the patio, drawn on a grid. Each grid square represents 1 square foot.

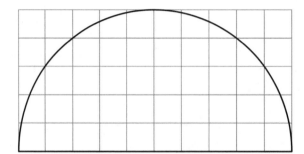

a. What is the area of the patio? Explain how you found the area.

b. Each quart of nonslip paint covers 32 square feet. How much paint should Lydia's stepmother buy if she plans to put one coat of paint on the patio? Keep a record of your work.

c. To keep grass from growing onto the patio, Lydia wants to plant a border around the patio. Since the patio is against the house, she only needs a border around the curved edge. How long will the border be? Show how you found your answer.

4. Shown below are the relative sizes of a large tile and a small tile. When measured with large tiles, the area of a rectangular room is 12 square units and the perimeter is 16 units.

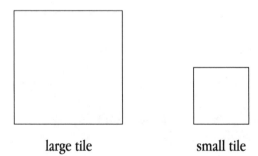

large tile   small tile

a. What would the area and perimeter of the room be (in tile units) if it were measured with the small tiles?

b. How do the measures you found in part a compare to the measures found by using the large tiles?

5. A neighbor asks you to help her design a rectangular pen for her dog, Ruff. Your neighbor has 42 meters of fencing to use for the pen.
   a. What design would give Ruff the most space for playing?

   b. What design would give Ruff the best space for running?

After looking at your designs, your neighbor decides to use her house as one of the walls for the pen. Her house is 35 meters long.

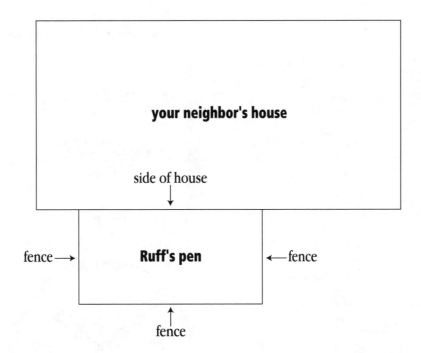

c. Using your neighbor's idea, now what design would give Ruff the most space for playing?

d. What design would give Ruff the best space for running?

6. The Acme sign company makes traffic signs for the state road commission. A model of the signs and their approximate measurements are given below.

YIELD

80 cm

85 cm

75 cm

SCHOOL ZONE

89 cm

126 cm

89 cm

SPEED LIMIT 55

75 cm

60 cm

96 cm

R R

92 cm

a. One of the costs that Acme must consider is the cost of metal. If metal costs $1.00 for every 1000 square centimeters, what is the cost of the metal for each sign?

Yield sign: _____

School zone sign: _____

Speed limit sign: _____

Railroad crossing sign: _____

b. After the signs are cut, the edges must be sanded to prevent metal splinters. If the cost of sanding is 2 cents for every centimeter, what will it cost to sand each sign?

Yield sign: _____

School zone sign: _____

Speed limit sign: _____

Railroad crossing sign: _____

7. Lara is helping her family build a recreation room in their basement. The room will be 28 feet by 20 feet. They have already put up the walls.

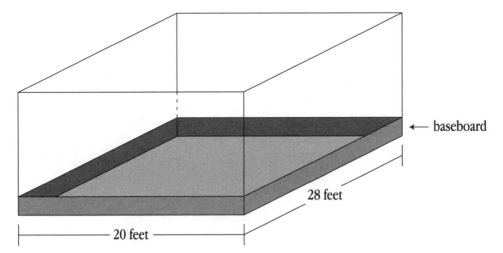

← baseboard

28 feet

20 feet

a. The family wants to tile the floor. Lara decides to buy 1-foot-square tiles. How many tiles will she need? Show your work.

b. The tiles Lara has chosen cost $0.75 each. How much will the tile floor cost? Show how you found your answer.

c. Lara needs to buy baseboard to put along the wall. How much baseboard does she need? Show how you found your answer.

d. The baseboard comes in 10-foot and 16-foot lengths. How many boards of each length should Lara buy? Show how you found your answer.

When you encounter problems like this in the real world, you will often have to consider several factors. Questions e–g look at conditions that Lara might think are important.

e. Suppose these are the prices of the baseboard.

Baseboard	
16-foot lengths	$1.25 per foot
10-foot lengths	$1.10 per foot

How many boards of each length should Lara buy if she wants to spend the least amount of money? Explain your answer.

f. When two sections of baseboard meet, they create a *seam*.

If Lara wants as few seams as possible, how many baseboards of each length should she buy?

g. If you were Lara, how many baseboards of each length would you buy?

Name _____ Date _____

1. Find the perimeter and area of each figure below. Explain your strategy for finding each answer.

   a.
   12 cm
   25 cm

   b.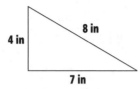
   4 in
   8 in
   7 in

   c.

   d.
   10 in

2. Each grid square at right is 1 centimeter by 1 centimeter. Jordan says that the area of the shape on the grid is about 25 square centimeters.

   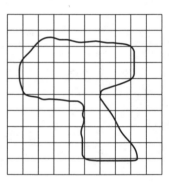

   a. How do you think Jordan's estimate compares to the actual area? Explain.

   b. Find your own estimate for the area of the shape. Explain your strategy.

3. Find the perimeter and area of the parallelogram below.

   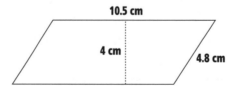
   10.5 cm
   4 cm
   4.8 cm

Unit Test

4. The table below shows lengths and widths of different rectangles.

Length	Width
1 cm	8 cm
2 cm	7 cm
3 cm	6 cm
4 cm	5 cm

    a. As you read down the table, are the areas of the rectangles constant or changing? Explain.

    b. As you read down the table, are the perimeters of the rectangles constant or changing? Explain.

5. A rectangle with an area of 30 square units has sides with whole-number lengths.

    a. Could the perimeter of the rectangle be 22 units? Explain your reasoning.

    b. Could the perimeter of the rectangle be 34 units? Explain your reasoning.

6. Find the perimeter and area of the figure below. Explain the strategy you use to find your answers.

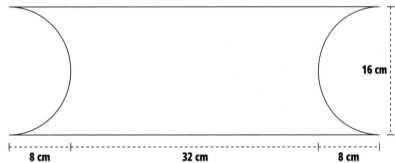

8 cm   32 cm   8 cm   16 cm

7. Irene drew a rectangle with an area of 196 square units. She finds that this is the largest area possible for any rectangle with the same perimeter.

    a. What are the dimensions of the rectangle? Explain your reasoning.

    b. What is the perimeter of the rectangle? Explain your reasoning.

Notebook Checklist

Journal Organization

_____ Problems and Mathematical Reflections are labeled and dated.

_____ Work is neat and easy to find and follow.

Vocabulary

_____ All words are listed.

_____ All words are defined or described.

Quizzes and Check-Ups

_____ Check-Up 1 _____ Quiz A

_____ Check-Up 2 _____ Quiz B

Homework Assignments

_____ _____

_____ _____

_____ _____

_____ _____

_____ _____

_____ _____

_____ _____

_____ _____

_____ _____

_____ _____

_____ _____

_____ _____

_____ _____

Self Assessment

Vocabulary

Of the vocabulary words I defined or described in my journal, the word _____ best demonstrates my ability to give a clear definition or description.

Of the vocabulary words I defined or described in my journal, the word _____ best demonstrates my ability to use an example to help explain or describe an idea.

Mathematical Ideas

1. a. I learned these things about the relationships between area and perimeter:

    b. I learned these things about how to find the area and perimeter of rectangles, parallelograms, triangles, and circles:

    c. Here are page numbers of journal entries that give evidence of what I have learned, along with descriptions of what each entry shows:

2. a. These are the mathematical ideas I am still struggling with:

    b. This is why I think these ideas are difficult for me:

    c. Here are page numbers of journal entries that give evidence of what I am struggling with, along with descriptions of what each entry shows:

Class Participation

I contributed to the classroom discussion and understanding of *Covering and Surrounding* when I . . .
(Give examples.)

Assessment Resources

for
How Likely Is It?

For the Quiz, each pair will need two chips marked with Xs and Ys as described in the quiz (bingo chips work nicely for this and can be written on with a permanent marker) and a small cup (shaking the chips in a cup instead of flipping them has proved easier for teachers to manage). Additionally, you will need to discuss with your students how each pair's results will be collected on a master chart that you create on the board so that pairs can analyze the entire class's data.

For the Unit Test, each student will need three chips marked with Xs, Ys, and Zs as described on the Unit Test, page 74, and a small cup. Again, students will be combining their data on a class chart and analyzing the entire class's data.

Name _____ Date _____

1. Use this circle to draw a spinner with six sections. Make the spinner so that it is equally likely that the spinner will land in each of the six sections. What fraction of the circle is each section?

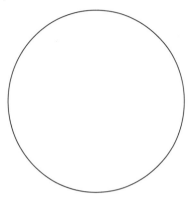

2. Use this circle to draw another spinner with six sections, but make this spinner so that it is *not* equally likely that the spinner will land in each of the six sections. What fraction of the circle is each section?

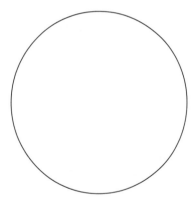

3. **a.** Give an example of an event that has a 100% chance of happening.

b. Give an example of an event that is impossible.

Check-Up 1

c. If an event is impossible, what are the chances that it will occur?

4. Rachel has tossed a fair coin ten times, and it has landed heads up every time.
   a. Is this possible? Explain.

   b. Is this likely? Explain.

   c. Which of the following statements is true about what will happen when Rachel tosses the coin again? Why?
      i.   The coin will land heads up.
      ii.   The coin will land tails up.
      iii. The chances of the coin landing heads up or tails up are equal.
      iv.   The coin is more likely to land heads up.
      v.   The coin is more likely to land tails up.

5. Two coins are flipped. Alan gets a point if the coins match, and Sondra gets a point if the coins do not match. Which of the following statements is true?
   a. Alan is more likely to win.
   b. Sondra is more likely to win.
   c. Alan and Sondra have the same chances of winning.
   d. There is not enough information to decide the chances of either player winning.
   e. Sondra can never win.

   Explain your answer.

Quiz

Your class has been asked by a game company to test their newest game, Flip 2 Chips. You and your classmates will be playing and analyzing the game. The company wants to know whether Flip 2 Chips is fair for all players.

Description of Flip 2 Chips

Materials: Two chips
- One chip has an **X** on both sides.
- One chip has an **X** on one side and a **Y** on the other side.

Small cup

Rules:
1. Shake the chips in the cup and then pour them out.
2. Award points according to what shows on the chips. *It does not matter who flipped the chips.*
   - Player A gets a point if the chips match.
   - Player B gets a point if the chips do not match.

---

1. From the description of the game, do you and your partner think Flip 2 Chips is a fair game of chance? _____ Explain your reasoning.

Names _____ Date _____

Play the game 20 times with your partner. Tally your results below.

Player A (match)	Player B (no match)

2.   From your results, do you think the game is fair? _____ Explain your reasoning.

Your teacher will set up a master chart on the board. Record your results—the number of matches and the number of nonmatches—on the chart. After all partners have recorded their data, examine the entire class's results.

3.   Based on the class's results, do you now think Flip 2 Chips is a fair game? _____ Explain your reasoning.

4.   Would you rather rely on your own data or the entire class's data to decide whether the game is fair? _____ Explain your reasoning.

Check-Up 2

1. The probability of a particular event is $\frac{3}{8}$. What is the probability that the event will not happen? Explain.

2. If two number cubes are tossed over and over again, what sum would you expect to occur most often? Explain.

3. Josh is tossing beanbags randomly onto this game mat. What is the probability of a beanbag landing in an area marked B?

```
+----------+----+----+
|          |  A |  B |
|    A     +----+----+
|          |  C |  A |
+----------+----+----+
|    B     |         |
+----------+    B    |
|    C     |         |
+----------+---------+
```

In 4 and 5, use the spinner to the right.

4. What is the probability of the spinner landing in a region marked A?

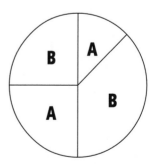

5. What is the probability of the spinner landing in a region marked B?

Check-Up 2

6. Fifty students in King Middle School were surveyed about their favorite sandwich. Here are the results of the survey:

Sandwich Preferences	
Peanut butter	32
Bologna	10
Cheese	7
Tuna fish	1

a. If a student is picked at random from the school, what is the probability that the student's favorite sandwich is peanut butter?

b. If a student is picked at random from the school, what is the probability that the student's favorite sandwich is *not* bologna?

c. If there are 550 students in the school, how many would you expect to say that cheese is their favorite sandwich?

7. A spinner is spun 100 times. The spinner landed on red 61 times and blue 39 times. How might the spinner be divided? Use this circle to draw a spinner that would be likely to give these results.

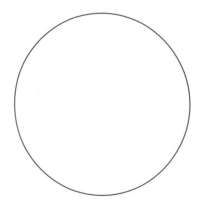

8. Which of the following numbers could not be a probability? Explain your answer.

$\frac{1}{3}$ 0 $\frac{8}{9}$ 1 $\frac{5}{4}$

Assign these questions as additional homework, or use them as review, quiz, or test questions.

1. a. Design a game—other than the Roller Derby game in your book—that uses two number cubes. Explain the rules, and give the number of players and the materials needed.

    b. Is your game a fair game of chance? Why or why not?

    c. Make up and answer at least two probability questions about your game.

2. Each box of Cocoablast cereal includes a Mad Mongo Monster action figure. There are four different action figures, and each figure has an equal chance of being put in a cereal box at the factory. Kalvin is trying to collect at least one of each figure. How many boxes of cereal do you think Kalvin will need to buy before he collects one of each figure? Find a way to investigate this question. Explain your methods and your reasoning.

3. John is going to flip three coins.

    a. What is the probability that all three coins will match? Explain your answer.

    b. What is the probability that there will be at least two heads? Explain your answer.

4. Think up a bag containing 20 of the same object, such as blocks or marbles, in three or four different colors.

    a. Describe the contents of the bag you are thinking about.

    b. Determine the theoretical probability of drawing each color by analyzing the bag's contents.

5. a. How many different ways are there to answer a true/false test that has four questions?

    b. If you were to guess at the four answers for the true/false test, what is the probability of getting all four right?

    c. If you were to guess at the four answers for the true/false test, what is the probability of getting at least two right?

6. You have been saving your money for a year and now have enough to buy a new bike. You want to make an informed decision, so you go to the library and read the most recent *Consumer Reports* magazine, which contains an article on models and makes of bikes. (*Consumer Reports* makes recommendations of the best product to buy based on a sampling of hundreds of owners—in this case, bike owners.)

    You also decide to talk to a few of your friends who have bought new bikes in the last year. Four of your friends like a certain model of bike that the *Consumer Reports* article did not highly recommend. Three other friends each recommended the model of bike that they own.

    a. Would you go with *Consumer Reports* magazine's recommendation, your four friends' recommendation, or an individual friend's recommendation?

    b. Explain your reasons for deciding whose recommendation you would follow.

Unit Test

1. Your class has been asked by a game company to test their new, exciting chip game, Flip 3 Chips. You will be playing and analyzing the game. The company wants to know whether the game is fair for all players.

Description of Flip 3 Chips

Materials: Three chips
- One chip has an X on one side and a Y on the other side.
- One chip has an X on one side and a Z on the other side.
- One chip has a Y on one side and a Z on the other side.

Small cup

Rules:
1. Shake the chips in the cup and then pour them out.
2. To score, award points by what shows on the chips. It does not matter who flipped the chips.
   - Player A gets a point if any two chips match.
   - Player B gets a point if all three chips are different.

---

a. From the description of the game, do you think Flip 3 Chips is a fair game of chance?_____
Explain your answer.

Play the game 20 times. Tally your results below.

Player A (2 chips match)	Player B (no chips match)

b. From your results, do you think the game is fair?_____ Explain your reasoning.

Unit Test

c. From your results, what is the probability of two chips matching?

d. From your results, what is the probability of no chips matching?

Your teacher will set up a master chart on the board. Record your results—the number of two chips matching and the number of no chips matching—on the chart. After all students have recorded their results, examine the entire class's results.

e. Based on the class's results, do you now think Flip 3 Chips is a fair game? From your results, do you think the game is fair?_____ Explain your reasoning.

f. From the class's results, what is the probability of two chips matching?

g. From the class's results, what is the probability of no chips matching?

h. What are all the possible outcomes that could result from flipping the chips?

Unit Test

    i. What is the theoretical probability of two chips matching?

    j. What is the theoretical probability of no chips matching?

    k. How do these two probabilities compare with the class's experimental probabilities?

2. A bag contains one green marble, two yellow marbles, four blue marbles, and five red marbles.

    a. What is the probability of randomly drawing a blue marble from the bag?

    b. What is the probability of not drawing a blue marble?

    c. If you double the number of green, yellow, blue, and red marbles in the bag, what will be the probability of drawing a blue marble?

   d. How does your answer for part c compare with your answer for part a? Explain.

   e. If you add two of each color to the original bag of marbles, what is the probability of drawing a blue marble?

   f. How does your answer for part e compare with your answer for part a? Explain.

   g. How many blue marbles would you need to add to the original bag of marbles to make the probability of drawing a blue marble $\frac{1}{2}$?

3. A gum machine contains orange, yellow, and purple gum balls. The probability of getting an orange gum ball is $\frac{3}{4}$. The probability of getting a yellow gum ball is $\frac{1}{6}$.

   a. What is the probability of getting a purple gum ball? Explain how you determined your answer.

   b. What is the fewest number of gum balls that could be in the machine?

   c. If there are 36 gum balls in the machine, how many are purple? How many are yellow? How many are orange?

Notebook Checklist

Journal Organization

_____ Problems and Mathematical Reflections are labeled and dated.

_____ Work is neat and easy to find and follow.

Vocabulary

_____ All words are listed.

_____ All words are defined or described.

Quiz and Check-Ups

_____ Check-Up 1   _____ Quiz

_____ Check-Up 2

Homework Assignments

_____ _____

_____ _____

_____ _____

_____ _____

_____ _____

_____ _____

_____ _____

_____ _____

_____ _____

_____ _____

_____ _____

_____ _____

_____ _____

_____ _____

Self-Assessment

Vocabulary

Of the vocabulary words I defined or described in my journal, the word _____ best demonstrates my ability to give a clear definition or description.

Of the vocabulary words I defined or described in my journal, the word _____ best demonstrates my ability to use an example to help explain or describe an idea.

Mathematical Ideas

1. a. In *How Likely Is It?* I learned these things about how to determine the probability that an event will happen:

    b. I learned these things about the difference between a possible event and a probable event:

    c. Here are page numbers of journal entries that give evidence of what I have learned, along with descriptions of what each entry shows:

2. a. These are the mathematical ideas I am still struggling with:

    b. This is why I think these ideas are difficult for me:

    c. Here are page numbers of journal entries that give evidence of what I am struggling with, along with descriptions of what each entry shows:

Class Participation

I contributed to the classroom discussion and understanding of *How Likely Is It?* when I . . .
(Give examples.)

Assessment Resources

for
Bits and Pieces II

The final assessment is a unit test consisting of two parts. The first part is done in class. The second part is a take-home portion. For the take-home part, students are to go through catalogs and find three different items they would like to order. Each item they select must cost at least $10.00. You might want to have a collection of catalogs for students who need them; perhaps solicit the help of your colleagues in gathering them.

Check-Up 1

1. Ms. Ngyen has a total of 150 students in her classes. Of these students, 30% eat during the first lunch period, 20% eat during the second lunch period, and the rest eat during the third lunch period. How many of her students eat during each lunch period?

2. Each week, Stewart saves $16 of his $48 paycheck. What percent of his pay does he save?

3. During the T-Shirt Shoppe's Fantastic Fall Sale, customers who buy an $8 t-shirt at the regular price get a second t-shirt at half price. Zahara bought two t-shirts during the sale. What percent did she save off the regular price?

4. Ted has a coupon for 50¢ off a jar of Sticky peanut butter. If a jar of the peanut butter is priced at $1.59, what percent of the cost will Ted save by using the coupon?

5. The total bill for drinks and a large pizza for three people is $14.90 before tax. The sales tax is 5%. The group wants to leave a 15% tip. How much should each person pay if they are to share the bill equally? Indicate whether you figured out the tip before or after the tax was added.

Check-Up 2

1. At D. J.'s Drink Stand, Erika ordered chocolate milk made in the following proportions: $\frac{1}{4}$ chocolate syrup, $\frac{2}{3}$ cold milk, and the rest whipped cream.

   a. What fraction of Erika's drink will be whipped cream?

   b. Erika changes her mind and decides that she wants the whipped cream in her drink replaced with cold milk. What fraction of her drink will be milk?

2. Gregorio made money over his summer vacation by mowing lawns. One week he worked the following schedule:

Monday	$5\frac{1}{2}$ hours
Tuesday	$3\frac{3}{4}$ hours
Wednesday	$4\frac{3}{4}$ hours
Thursday	$6\frac{1}{4}$ hours
Friday	$2\frac{3}{4}$ hours
Saturday	$2\frac{3}{4}$ hours

   How many hours did Gregorio work for the week?

Check-Up 2

3. Mr. Broadston took his cross-country team out for pizza. He ordered four medium pizzas, which were each cut into 12 pieces. The team ate the following amounts:

Scott ate $\frac{1}{3}$ of a pizza   Rusty ate $\frac{1}{2}$ of a pizza

Josh ate $\frac{7}{12}$ of a pizza   Da-Wei ate $\frac{5}{12}$ of a pizza

Darin ate $\frac{2}{12}$ of a pizza   Alex ate $\frac{2}{3}$ of a pizza

Mr. Broadston ate $\frac{1}{12}$ of a pizza

   a. How many pizzas did the team eat?

   b. How many pizzas were left?

   c. What is the difference between the amount of pizza eaten and the amount of pizza left uneaten?

Name _____ Date _____

Check-Up 3

1. On a particular map of Denmark, 1 inch on the map represents 12 miles.

    a. What does $2\frac{1}{2}$ inches on the map represent?

    b. What does $3\frac{3}{4}$ inches on the map represent?

2. A winter sports pass at Wood Middle School costs $15.00. A student without a pass must pay $1.75 for each event. How many sports events would a student have to attend to make the pass a better deal?

3. If each person in North America produces $3\frac{2}{3}$ pounds of garbage a day, how many pounds of garbage does each person produce in a year?

Check-Up 3

4. Derek and Conor work for two different radio stations. Derek makes $15.75 an hour. Conor makes $12.25 an hour for a 20-hour work week, but he is paid time and a half for any time he works over 20 hours. (*Time and a half* means Conor is paid $1\frac{1}{2}$ times his hourly wage for each overtime hour.) If Derek and Conor both work 30 hours one week, how much does each make?

5. Paula had $\frac{2}{3}$ of a pan of brownies left. She took the brownies to school, and her friends ate $\frac{3}{4}$ of them.

   a. How much of the pan of brownies did her friends eat?

   b. How much of the pan of brownies was left?

Assign these questions as additional homework, or use them as review, quiz, or test questions.

1. Find out what your local sales tax is. Ingrid purchased a product in your area and was charged 63¢ for sales tax. Give three possible amounts the product could have cost.

2. Michel and Benita are making a square dartboard for the school carnival. They want to paint the board so that it is 30% red, 20% green, 40% yellow, and 10% blue.

   a. Design a square dartboard that fits Michel and Benita's requirements.

   b. Benita decided that a circle would be better for the game. Make a circular dartboard that satisfies the same color requirements given above.

   c. Which dartboard would you rather use?

   d. Which dartboard was easier to design? Why?

3. McDonald's farmstand sells eggs for 80¢ a dozen.

   a. How much would $3\frac{1}{2}$ dozen eggs cost?

   b. How much would $\frac{3}{4}$ of a dozen eggs cost?

4. Suppose that the Pizza Pirate ate $\frac{1}{3}$ of a pizza the first night and $\frac{1}{4}$ of what remained every night after that. How many nights would it take until the pizza was half gone? Drawing a picture might help you explain your reasoning.

5. a. What happens to the size of a fraction between 0 and 1 when you add the same number to the numerator and the denominator? For example, if you start with $\frac{1}{2}$ and add 1 to the numerator and the denominator, and you get $\frac{2}{3}$. Choose other fractions between 0 and 1, and add the same number to the numerator and the denominator. How do the new fractions compare to the fractions you started with? What patterns do you notice?

   b. How does the fraction you get by adding the same number to both the numerator and denominator of a fraction *greater than 1* (for example, $\frac{6}{5}$) compare to the fraction you started with?

   c. How does the new fraction you get by multiplying the numerator and denominator of a fraction by the same number compare to the fraction you started with? You may want to try several fractions and look for patterns.

   d. What happens when you add or multiply the numerator and denominator of a fraction that is equivalent to 1 by the same number?

   e. Summarize what you know from the work you did in this problem.

6. The cost of renting a drum set is a $25 initial fee, plus $35.95 a month. How much will it cost to rent a drum set for a year?

7. The local youth group has decided to run a summer baby-sitting program to earn money for the club and for the individuals in the club. The baby-sitting program will run from 9:00 A.M. to 4:30 P.M. Monday through Friday. The youth-group leader and student officers must develop a plan for the program. (When answering the following questions, show enough of your work so that someone reading it can follow how you solved the problems.)

   a. Jin Lee, Sarah, Jesse, and Alex are assigned to the toddler room for the month of July. Two students must work in this room at all times. They decide to share the workload equally. How many hours will each of them work each week?

   b. If students are paid $3.75 an hour, how much will each of these students be paid for a week of work?

   c. Set up a work schedule for Jin Lee, Sarah, Jesse, and Alex for a week in July.

   d. Jin Lee and Sarah decide to make a pancake breakfast for the six morning workers who work in the toddler room, the preschool room, and the kindergarten room. They found a recipe that will make 12 silver-dollar pancakes per batch. They figure that they need 30 silver-dollar pancakes, 5 per person. How much of each ingredient will they need to make 30 silver-dollar pancakes?

Silver-Dollar Pancakes

$1\frac{1}{4}$ cups flour

1 egg

3 teaspoons baking powder

$1\frac{1}{2}$ tablespoons sugar

$\frac{1}{2}$ teaspoon salt

$\frac{3}{4}$ cup milk

2 tablespoons salad oil

Makes 12 silver-dollar pancakes.

---

8. In stage 1 below, the middle one third of a line segment is covered by a triangle. In stage 2, the middle one third of each of the two parts that were uncovered in stage 1 are covered. In stage 3, the middle one third of each of the parts that were not covered in stage 3 are covered.

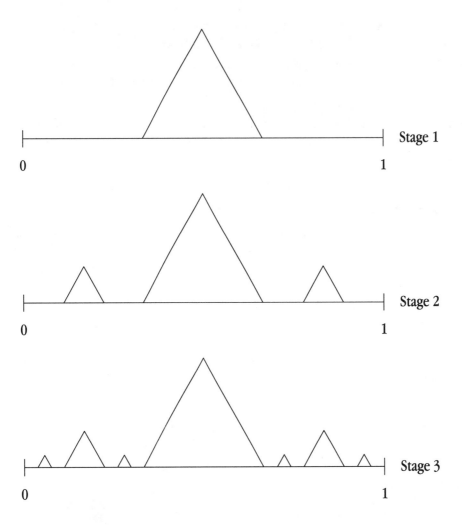

a. What fraction of the line is covered at stage 1? What fraction of the line is *not* covered?

b. What fraction of the line is covered at stage 2? What fraction of the line is *not* covered?

c. What fraction of the line is covered at stage 3? What fraction of the line is *not* covered?

Unit Test: In-Class Portion

1. Troy is going to basketball camp. Before he goes, he needs to buy some things. He and his parents agree that he can buy two pairs of shorts, four t-shirts, six pairs of socks, and a jacket. Shop Easy has everything they need for the following prices:

   Shorts $7.98 each

   T-shirts $6.35—on sale: buy one at the regular price, and get a second at half price

   Socks $1.98 for two pairs

   Jackets $19.99 each

   a. How much will the total bill for Troy's clothes be, including sales tax? (Figure sales tax based on what is charged in your area.)

   b. Troy had $100 when he started his shopping. Did he have enough money? If so, how much extra? If not, how much was he short?

Unit Test: In-Class Portion

2. Kristine, a high-school student, works part time at the dry cleaners. Her take-home check is $80 every two weeks. She has set up this budget for herself:

$\frac{1}{3}$ of her paycheck goes into her college savings account

$\frac{1}{4}$ of her paycheck is for clothing

$\frac{1}{6}$ of her paycheck is for snacks

$\frac{1}{4}$ of her paycheck is for entertainment and recreational activities with friends

   a. What dollar amount of her paycheck goes to

      savings? _____   clothing? _____

      snacks? _____   entertainment? _____

   b. Make a circle graph showing Kristine's budget.

Unit Test: In-Class Portion

3. Elizabeth is shopping for a new winter coat. She finds the coat that she likes the best in two different stores.

- In the first store, the coat is priced at $84, but a sale sign states that the coat is $\frac{1}{3}$ off.
- In the second store, the coat is priced at $76, but a sale sign states that the coat is $\frac{1}{4}$ off.

Store 1   Store 2

a. From which store should Elizabeth buy the coat if she wants to spend the least amount of money?

b. Elizabeth's mother finds the same coat in a catalog. The coat is priced the same as the regular price at the store from which Elizabeth has decided to buy (based on your results to part a), but the catalog has the coat on sale for 30% off. In addition, Elizabeth's mother has a coupon for $5.00 off any purchase from the catalog. Any catalog order has a shipping charge of 6% of the price of an item. Which is the better buy, the coat at the store or the coat in the catalog?

Unit Test: In-Class Portion

4. How many bows can you make from 5 meters of ribbon if a bow takes $\frac{1}{4}$ of a meter of ribbon?

5. If a toy store offers an additional 25% discount on board games that have already been reduced by 30%, will the final cost be the same as a discount of 55% on the original price? Work through an example to help explain your answer.

Unit Test: Take-Home Miniproject

Ordering from a Catalog

1. Find three different items you would like to order from a catalog. Each item must cost at least $10.00. On the back of your paper, tape or glue the picture of the item and its description, or draw a picture of the item and write out its description. Include the price.

2. Complete the attached order form as if you were ordering your three items from the C. M. Project catalog. On the back of the order form, show all the work you did to calculate the amounts for shipping and tax.

3. **a.** Choose one of the items you ordered. List the item with a brief description and give its price.

   b. What would this item cost if it were on sale for 25% off? Show how you found your answer.

   c. What would the item cost if it were on sale for $\frac{1}{3}$ off? Show how you found your answer.

4. Suppose another catalog has your first item listed for $5.00 less than the price you have listed. A third catalog has your item marked down 20%. If shipping charges and tax are the same, which is the better deal for you, and why?

Name _____ Date _____

C.M. Project Catalog
Order Form

Shipping Address

Name _____
Address _____
City _____ State _____ Zip Code _____
Phone ( )

To speed up your order, use our toll-free number 24 hours a day, 7 days a week—100% of the time! 1-800-PER-CENT

Item No.	Description	Size	Color	Qty.	Price/Unit	Total
			Merchandise Total			
			Shipping (10% of Merchandise Total)			
			Tax (_____%)			
			TOTAL			

Method of Payment

☐ Charge to:
_____ VISA _____ MASTERCARD
Credit Card # _____
Expiration Date _____/_____/_____

☐ Check or Money Order

Signature _____

Name _____ Date _____

Journal Organization

_____ Problems and Mathematical Reflections are labeled and dated.

_____ Work is neat and easy to find and follow.

Vocabulary

_____ All words are listed.   _____ All words are defined and described.

Quizzes and Check-Ups

_____ Check-Up 1   _____ Check-Up 3

_____ Check-Up 2   _____ Unit Test

Homework Assignments

_____ _____

_____ _____

_____ _____

_____ _____

_____ _____

_____ _____

_____ _____

_____ _____

_____ _____

_____ _____

_____ _____

_____ _____

_____ _____

_____ _____

_____ _____

_____ _____

_____ _____

Self-Assessment

Vocabulary

Of the vocabulary words I defined or described in my journal, the word _____ best demonstrates my ability to give a clear definition or description.

Of the vocabulary words I defined or described in my journal, the word _____ best demonstrates my ability to use an example to help explain or describe an idea.

Mathematical Ideas

1. **a.** I learned these things about adding, subtracting, and multiplying fractions and decimals:

   b. I learned these things about working with percents:

   c. Here are page numbers of journal entries that give evidence of what I have learned, along with descriptions of what each entry shows:

2. **a.** These are the mathematical ideas I am still struggling with:

   b. This is why I think these ideas are difficult for me:

   c. Here are page numbers of journal entries that give evidence of what I am struggling with, along with descriptions of what each entry shows:

Class Participation

I contributed to the classroom discussion and understanding of *Bits and Pieces II* when I . . . (Give examples.)

Assessment Resources

for
Ruins of Montarek

Check-Up 1

1. The right view of a building is given below. Which of the views is the left view? _____

a.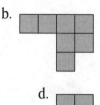

b.

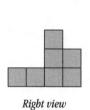

Right view

c.

d.

e.

In 2 and 3, use the base plan and views shown below.

a.

b.

e.

2		
3	1	2
1		1

Front

c.

d.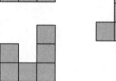

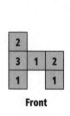

2. Picture the building that the base plan describes. Which view is the front view of the building? _____

3. Picture the building that the base plan describes. Which view is the right view of the building? _____

Check-Up 1

4. A base plan for a building is given at right.
   On the grids below, draw a set of building plans—
   a base outline, a front view, and a right view—
   for the building.

Front

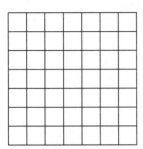

Base outline

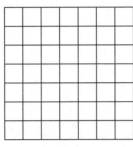

Front view

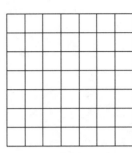

Right view

5. The base outline, front view, and right view of a building are given below. On the grid, draw a base plan for a building that fits this set of plans.

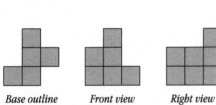

Base outline   *Front view*   *Right view*

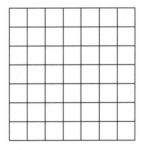

6. Picture a building that has the front and right views shown below.
   • Draw the base outline of your building.
   • Create a base plan by numbering the squares of your base outline.

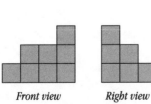

Front view   *Right view*

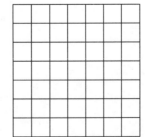

Check-Up 1

7. Look at the set of building plans shown below.

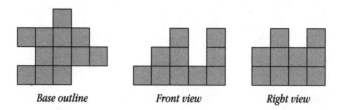

Base outline   Front view   Right view

a. On the grid below, draw a base plan for a *minimal building* that fits the building plans. How many cubes are needed to construct a minimal building for these plans? _____

b. Now draw a base plan for a *maximal building* that fits the building plans. How many cubes are needed to construct a maximal building for these plans? _____

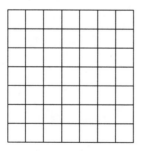

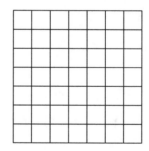

Minimal building   Maximal building

Check-Up 2

1. Which isometric drawing shows the view from the left front corner of the building represented by the base plan below? _____

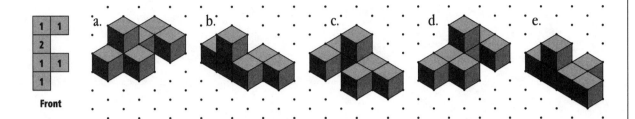

2. Which isometric drawing shows the view from the back left corner of the building represented by the base plan below? _____

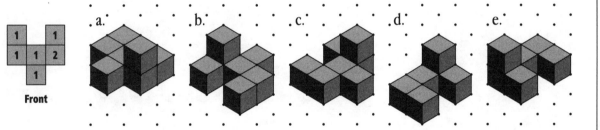

3. Which drawing is not a view of the building shown below? _____

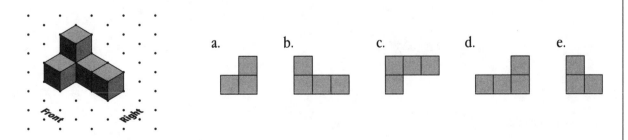

Check-Up 2

4. The isometric drawing below shows a building from the front right corner. Which drawing shows the back view of the building? _____

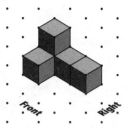

a.   b.   c.   d.   e.

5. The isometric drawing below shows a building from the front right corner. Which drawing shows the right view of the building? _____

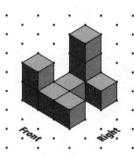

a.   b.   c.   d.   e.

6. Draw the isometric view from the right back corner of the building represented by the base plan below.

Front

Check-Up 2

7. Draw the building that would remain if the shaded cubes were removed from the building below.

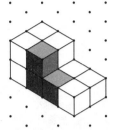

8. Which of the buildings below can be made from the two basic shapes shown?

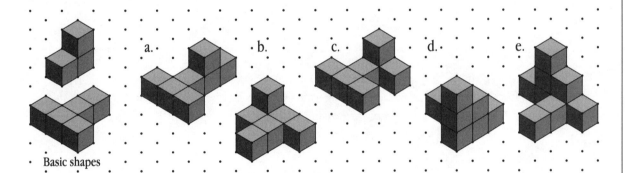

Basic shapes   a.   b.   c.   d.   e.

9. How many cubes are needed to build this rectangular solid?

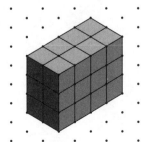

Quiz

1. In her last expedition to Montarek, Emily Hawkins found a stone tablet containing this set of building plans.

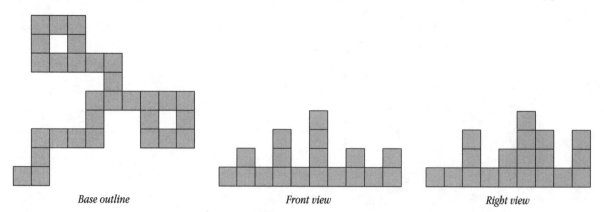

Base outline   *Front view*   *Right view*

    a. Construct a maximal building for this set of plans. Make a base plan of your building by numbering the squares in the base outline.

    b. How many cubes did your building require? _____

2. Below are base plans for three different buildings. The next page shows isometric drawings of the three buildings from each corner. Match each building with its corner views. Label each corner view with the building number and the corner—front right, right back, back left, or left front—from which the building is being viewed. Put your labels on the lines provided.

Building 1

2	1	1
	3	1
	2	

Front

Building 2

1	2	1
	3	1
	2	

Front

Building 3

1	1	2
	3	1
	2	

Front

Quiz

a. Building _____

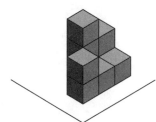

b. Building _____

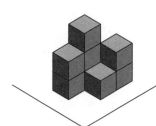

c. Building _____

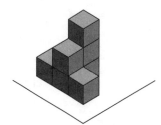

d. Building _____

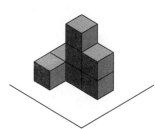

e. Building _____

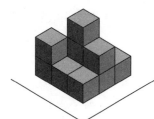

f. Building _____

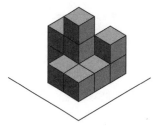

g. Building _____

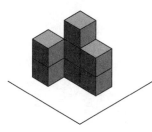

h. Building _____

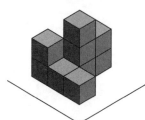

i. Building _____

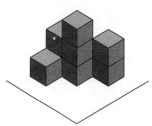

j. Building _____

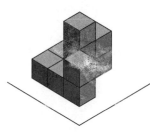

k. Building _____

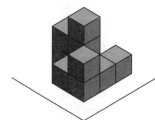

l. Building _____

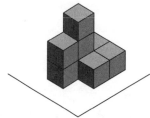

Assign these questions as additional homework, or use them as review, quiz, or test questions.

In 1 and 2, draw the mirror image of the figure on the other side of the mirror line.

1.

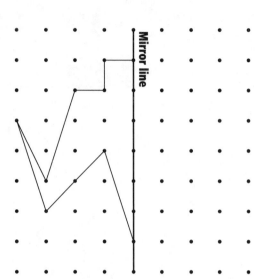

2.

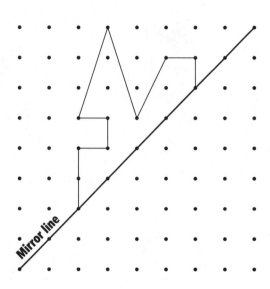

3. The base plan of a building is given below. Which of the given views is the left view? _____

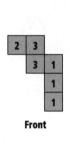

Front

a.

b.

e.

c.

d.

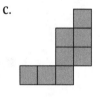

4. The back view of a building is given below. Which of the given views is the front view? _____

Back view

a.

b.

e.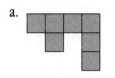

c.

d.

5. Below is a set of building plans.

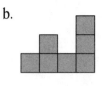

Base outline *Front view* *Right view*

Which of the base plans below can be completed to match the building in the plans? _____

a.

b.

c.

d.

e.

6. The base outline and front view of a building are given at right. Which of the views below could be a left view of the building? _____

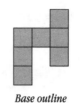

Base outline   *Front view*

a.

b.

e.

c.

d.

7. How many different views of the shape below can be drawn on isometric dot paper if the shape can be turned freely? _____

Draw as many views of the shape as you can on isometric dot paper.

8. Which of the buildings below can be made from the two basic shapes shown? _____

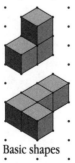

a.

b.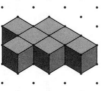

c.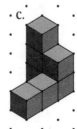

d.

e.

Basic shapes

9. **a.** What is the maximum number of cubes that could be used to make the building below? _____

   b. What is the minimum number of cubes needed to make the building below? _____

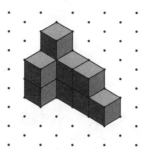

10. One view of a building is given at left below. From the drawings, find another view of the building. _____

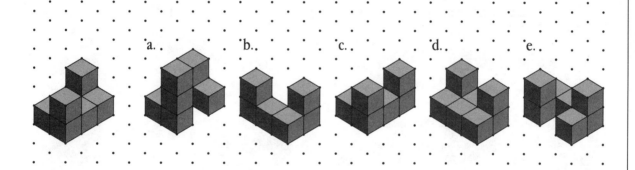

11. A base plan of a building is given below. Which of the following is *not* a corner view of the building? _____

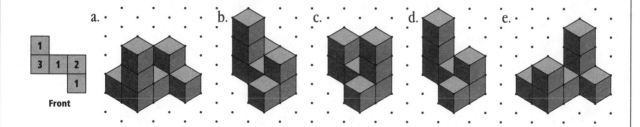

12. If a cube were added to the white face of the building given below, what would the new building look like?
_____

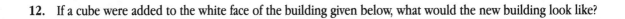

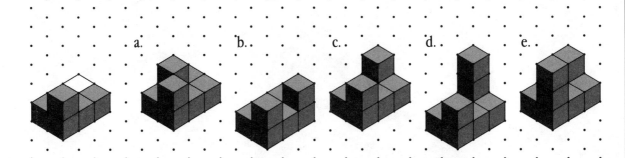

13. If the white cubes were removed from the building shown below, what would the new building look like?
_____

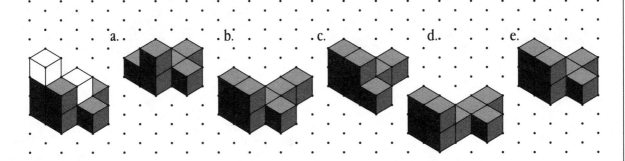

Name _____ Date _____

Unit Test

1. Make a cube model of the building shown in this base plan:

Front

   a. Sketch a set of building plans for the building on grid paper. Remember that a set of building plans includes the base outline, the front view, and the right view.

   b. Add as many cubes as you can to the building to make a different building that has the same set of building plans. Make a base plan of your new building.

   c. Explain how your new building can have the same set of building plans as the original building even though your new building has a different base plan.

2. The base outline and right view of a building are shown below. Of the three front views below, which is *not* possible for a building with the given base outline and right view? Explain your reasoning.

  a. b. c.

Base outline *Right view* *Front view* *Front view* *Front view*

3. Melinda has sketched this set of building plans on grid paper:

Base outline *Front view* *Right view*

   a. Melinda has built a building with 12 cubes that fits the above set of plans. Sketch a base plan of a building that uses 12 cubes that fits Melinda's set of building plans.

   b. Do you think that your base plan is exactly the same as the base plan for Melinda's building? Explain why or why not.

   c. Could you use more than 12 cubes to make a building that fits Melinda's building plans? If so, what is the greatest number of cubes you could use for a building that fits Melinda's building plans? If not, explain why 12 cubes is the greatest number of cubes you can use to make a building that fits Melinda's building plans.

Unit Test

4. For each of the cube buildings shown below, make a sketch on isometric dot paper of what the building would look like if the shaded cube(s) were removed.

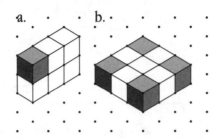

a. b.

5. Make a sketch on isometric dot paper to show what the building made from the base plan below would look like.

3	3	3
3	3	3
3	3	3

Name _____ Date _____

Journal Organization

_____ Problems and Mathematical Reflections are labeled and dated.

_____ Work is neat and easy to find and follow.

Vocabulary

_____ All words are listed.

_____ All words are defined or described.

Quizzes and Check-Ups

_____ Check-Up 1 _____ Quiz _____ Check-Up 2 _____ Unit Test

Homework Assignments

_____ _____

_____ _____

_____ _____

_____ _____

_____ _____

_____ _____

_____ _____

_____ _____

_____ _____

_____ _____

_____ _____

_____ _____

_____ _____

Self-Assessment

Vocabulary

Of the vocabulary words I defined or described in my journal, the word _____ best demonstrates my ability to give a clear definition or description.

Of the vocabulary words I defined or described in my journal, the word _____ best demonstrates my ability to use an example to help explain or describe an idea.

Mathematical Ideas

1. a. In *Ruins of Montarek*, I developed these skills for representing three-dimensional objects on paper:

    b. Here are page numbers of journal entries that give evidence of what I have learned, along with descriptions of what each entry shows:

2. a. These are the spatial skills I am still struggling with:

    b. This is why I think these ideas are difficult for me:

    c. Here are page numbers of journal entries that give evidence of what I am struggling with, along with descriptions of what each entry shows:

Class Participation

I contributed to the classroom discussion and understanding of *Ruins of Montarek* when I...
(Give examples.)